Contents

Written by
Julia Golding

Illustrated by
Sonia Possentini

Series editor **Dee Reid**

ALWAYS LEARNIN

Before reading *The Choice*

Characters

Gideon

AJ

Dan's Sister

Dan

Tricky words

ch1	**p4**	decision
ch1	**p6**	replica
ch1	**p8**	ignore
ch1	**p8**	annoying

ch2	**p10**	stash
ch3	**p13**	possession
ch4	**p16**	shrugged

Introduction

Gideon is a dark angel. He was kicked out of heaven for breaking the rules. Now he tries to use his powers as an angel to help people on earth. If he can do enough good on earth he might be allowed back to heaven. One day Gideon meets AJ. AJ is about to make the biggest decision of his life.

The Choice

Chapter One

My name is Gideon. I am a dark angel. I was

kicked out of heaven for breaking the rules. Now

I spend my time trying to help humans.

AJ is one of the humans I tried to help. When

I first saw AJ, he was outside the fish and chip

shop eating a big bag of chips.

As I got close to AJ, I saw the light come on over his head. I don't mean the street lamp. I mean the light only angels can see. We see this light when humans are about to make a decision that will change their lives for ever. I looked around. I couldn't see any angels from heaven coming to help AJ. He was on his own unless I stepped in. I thought it would be easier to chat to AJ if I had a bag of chips but it turned out to be a mistake to go into the chip shop first.

While I was paying for my chips, I saw two boys and a girl go up to AJ. The boys were older and taller than AJ. They took him into a corner. The girl was very upset.

One good thing about being an angel, even a dark angel, is that we can hear what humans are saying even if we're not standing near them, so I could hear what they said to AJ.

"Dan and I went to see Mikey and Mikey started on us," said the taller of the boys. "When Mikey punched Dan," he went on, "Dan pointed what he thought was a replica gun at Mikey."

"I only wanted to scare him," said Dan. "I swear I didn't even know the gun was real."

"The gun went off and Mikey got hit," said the girl, sounding upset.

AJ looked shocked. "What are you going to do now?" he asked.

"We need you to keep the gun hidden for us," said Dan.

"Don't do this, AJ," said the girl. "It's stupid."

"Ignore my annoying little sister," said Dan, handing AJ the weapon. AJ quickly put it in his inside pocket.

As he walked away, Dan said, "I'll be in touch. Until then, keep the gun hidden and keep quiet."

So that's why the light had come on over AJ's head, I thought.

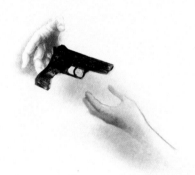

Chapter Two

Another cool thing about being an angel is that I can melt into the shadows when I want to, so no one could see me watching AJ's house. And if I close my eyes, I can see what AJ can see.

I saw him going from room to room looking for a place to stash the gun. He finally stopped outside Jonas's bedroom. Jonas is AJ's older brother. He's a quiet seventeen year old who has never been in any kind of trouble with the police.

AJ was thinking: *Mum is always checking out my bedroom to make sure I'm not getting into trouble. But she never goes through Jonas's stuff so she won't find the gun if I hide it here.*

AJ stashed the gun at the bottom of Jonas's wardrobe. He felt pleased. *Dan and Brad will respect me now*, he thought.

After a couple of hours, AJ's mum and Jonas came home. Then I saw that I wasn't the only person watching the house.

Chapter Three

Two police officers were in the alley opposite. I dipped into their thoughts. They had been given a tip-off that the gun had been stashed at this address. They were waiting for back up before making their move.

A police car rolled up, lights flashing. AJ's mum answered the door and let the officers inside. Half an hour later, they left with Jonas under arrest for possession of a lethal weapon. AJ's mum followed in her car, leaving AJ alone in the house.

Sometimes only the direct approach will work.

I knocked on the door. AJ opened it a crack.

"What do you want?" he said.

I could tell AJ wasn't worried about his brother. He was only worried about how he was going to tell Dan that the police had the gun.

"Hello, AJ. Can I come in?" I asked.

"No way! I'm not letting a stranger into the house," said AJ.

"But I'm not really a stranger. I know you very well indeed, Alexander Jackson. I'm your guardian angel."

Chapter Four

AJ tried to shut the door but I put my foot in

the way. "You have a scar on your elbow where

you broke your arm falling off your bike when

you were eight," I said, "and you go mad if you

see a wasp."

"Who told you that?" demanded AJ.

"I know everything about you because I can get inside your head," I said. "That's what a guardian angel can do. Right now you're thinking that you are in trouble with Dan. You think Jonas will be OK because he has never been in trouble with the police before. What you don't realise is that Jonas knows it was you and he doesn't want you to end up in trouble. So he won't tell tales on his younger brother. He will take the rap while you go free."

AJ shrugged. "So what?"

Sometimes I would like to blast thick-headed humans with an angel bolt. "Don't you care at all about your brother?" I shouted at AJ.

"The police have nothing on Jonas," said
AJ. "They'll believe the gun was planted by
someone else."

I tried another way to get through to AJ. "Don't
you care about all the harm that gun has done?"

AJ gave another shrug. He just didn't get it.
No amount of argument would work on
him; he had to *feel* it. I reached out and
touched his forehead. The history of the
gun flowed down through my fingertip and
into his brain. AJ saw each shooting, each
victim.

He saw the man killed in a drug deal; the youth shot in a drive-by because he was in the wrong part of the estate; the boy who had ended up in hospital today because of a stupid fight.

I made sure AJ felt the pain of every bullet, the grief of those left behind, the stupidity of it all. AJ slumped to the floor, the suffering was almost too much to bear.

"So," I said to AJ, "you have a choice. Are you going to leave your brother in jail and protect those boys who are too scared to own up to what they've done?"

"I didn't know all that about the gun," said AJ quietly. "I just wanted Dan and Brad to respect me."

"I know," I replied, "but are you brave enough to do the right thing by Jonas?"

I left AJ to make his choice. A few minutes later I saw him come out of the house and set off for the police station.

Quiz

Text comprehension

Literal comprehension

p7 What do Dan and the other boy need AJ to do for them?

p10 Why did AJ stash the gun in Jonas's room?

p15 How did Gideon prove that he knew all about AJ?

Inferential comprehension

p14 Why does Gideon use AJ's full name – Alexander Jackson?

p16 How can you tell that Jonas is a very loyal brother?

p17 What power does Gideon have in his fingertip?

Personal response

- What do you think of Gideon's way of making AJ see the harm the gun has done?
- What do you think AJ will say at the police station?
- Do you think there could be such things as guardian angels?

Author's style

p16 What words does the author use to show that Gideon is angry?

p18 What punctuation mark is used to separate the clauses?

p20 Which adverb does the author use to show that AJ is shocked about the harm the gun has done?

Characters

- **Brad**
- **AJ**
- **Dan**
- **Josie** (Dan's younger sister)

Setting the scene

AJ wants to seem cool to some of the older boys like Brad and Dan who live on his estate. Brad and Dan have been involved in an argument that went horribly wrong. They want AJ to help them so this is AJ's chance to impress them.

Brad: Hey AJ, how are you doing?

AJ: I'm OK. Are you OK, Dan? You look bad!

Dan: I'm not so good.

Josie: Not so good? It's a lot worse than not so good!

AJ: Why? What's happened?

Josie: You know I went out with Mikey?

AJ: Yeah.

Josie: Dan decided Mikey should have asked him first if it was OK.

Dan: Someone told me that Mikey danced with you at the Youth Club. No one goes out with my little sister without me saying it's OK!

Josie: How could he ask you if it was OK? He doesn't even know you. Anyway, you're my brother, not my mum!

Brad: So Dan and I went to see Mikey to sort him out but before we had a chance to explain why we were there, he started on us.

Josie: *(looking scared)* But the worst thing was that Dan found what he thought was a replica gun in an abandoned car a few days ago. He's been carrying it around in his bag, trying to decide what to do with it. I told him he should have handed it in to the police!

Brad: So when Mikey punched Dan, Dan pointed the gun at him.

Dan: I only wanted to scare him. I swear I didn't even know it was real.

Josie: The gun went off and Mikey got hit.

AJ: Is Mikey OK?

Brad: It's not as bad as it could have been. The bullet hit him in the leg. He's in hospital and he's going to be fine.

AJ: That's something I suppose.

Dan: Yeah, well Mikey knew the rules and he broke them.

Brad: What happened was an accident but it served Mikey right.

AJ: So what are you going to do now?

Josie: I've told them they should tell the police. Tell them that it was an accident.

Dan: They won't believe me. And anyway, as long as you don't tell Mikey who I am, the police will never know it was me.

Josie: I'm staying out of this. You've still got the gun and the police will find it in the end.

Brad: That's why we're here. We need you to do something for us, AJ. Can we trust you?

AJ: You can trust me, I swear.

Josie: Leave AJ out of this! It's nothing to do with him.

Dan: We are counting on you. You won't turn us in to the police?

AJ: I won't turn you in. What do you need me to do?

Brad: We need someone we can trust to hide this gun for us.

Dan: Keep it hidden until we come for it.

Brad: Don't tell anyone. We'll be in so much trouble if you do.

AJ: Don't worry, I can think of a good place to hide it.

Brad: It's better if you do it. The police can't do much as you're underage.

AJ: I have a place to hide it no one will suspect.

Josie: Don't do this, AJ. It's stupid. You don't need to get involved.

Dan: Ignore my annoying little sister. Keep the gun until we come for it. OK?

AJ: Alright.

(Dan gives AJ the gun)

Brad: Don't look so scared. It'll be fine.

Dan: Thanks for this, AJ.

Josie: I still think you should tell the police.

Dan: I'll be in touch once I've decided what to do with the gun. Until then, keep it hidden and keep quiet.

Quiz

Text comprehension

p24 What did Josie think Dan should have done with the gun?

p26 Why do you think AJ is so keen to help Dan and Brad?

p28 Why did Dan and Brad choose AJ to help them?

Vocabulary

p24 Find a word meaning 'a close copy'.

p25 Find a word meaning 'something that wasn't meant to happen'.

p28 Find a word meaning 'irritating'.

Before reading *CHAIN REACTION*

Find out about

• how one bad decision can set off a chain of events.

New vocabulary

p33 traditional   **p37** Chaos Theory
p36 harmless   **p37** reaction
p37 consequences

Introduction

Sometimes one bad decision can lead to lots of other things going wrong. This often happens in stories or films but it happens in real life too. In science, when tiny actions have big consequences, it is called 'Chaos Theory'.

CHAIN REACTION

Have you ever made one bad decision that set off a chain of events which nearly ended in disaster? If you have, you are not the only one. There are many stories going right back in time in which one bad decision leads to disaster.

King Midas turning his daughter to gold.

In a Greek myth, one of the gods lets King Midas choose a reward for doing something good. Midas chooses as his reward that everything he touches turns to gold. At first, Midas turns twigs and stones to gold. But then he touches his dog, and then his daughter. Both his daughter and his dog turn to gold. Midas asks the god to take away his reward. His bad choice of a reward nearly meant he lost his daughter.

In many traditional stories one bad decision nearly leads to disaster. In the story 'Beauty and the Beast', a man steals a rose from the Beast's garden to give to his daughter. The Beast catches him and, on pain of death, the man has to agree to give the Beast the first living thing that he sees when he gets home. The man thinks the first thing he will see will be his dog but instead it is Beauty, his daughter. Stealing one little rose nearly leads to disaster but, because this is a traditional story, it all ends happily ever after!

In the film 'Spider-Man', Peter Parker gets super powers when he is bitten by a spider. He has to decide whether he is going to use his powers to do good or to do evil. One of the decisions he makes sets off a chain of events which ends in disaster.

Peter Parker decides to go in for a cage fight for money.

He uses his super powers to win the fight.

The man who set up the fight will not pay Peter Parker because it wasn't a good fight.

Then that man is robbed and Peter Parker chooses not to use his super powers to stop the thief.

Then that thief shoots Peter Parker's uncle.

Would his uncle still have been shot if Peter Parker had decided to use his super powers to stop the thief?

In many comedy programmes a character makes a tiny decision that sets off a chain of events. 'Mr Bean' programmes start with Mr Bean doing something harmless, like going on holiday. One little thing goes wrong and then everything else goes wrong and Mr Bean causes chaos for all the people around him.

Mr Bean

Chaos Theory

It's not only in film and TV that little actions spark a chain of events. In science, there is a theory called the 'Chaos Theory' which describes chain reactions. This theory shows how tiny actions can have big consequences. The theory is that if, somewhere in the world, a butterfly flutters its wings, it moves the air a tiny bit. That tiny action has a reaction and it makes something else happen and, bit by bit, the reactions get bigger and bigger and you end up with a hurricane somewhere else in the world!

The First World War, in which nearly 37 million people died, was sparked by the shooting of an Austrian prince in 1914. This was the tiny action that had big consequences. When countries learned of the shooting of the prince they decided this meant war. One by one the countries moved their armies into position and, like a row of dominoes falling, the war could not be stopped.

Quiz

Text comprehension

Literal comprehension
p32 What reward did King Midas ask for?

p35 What is the consequence of Peter Parker not stopping the thief?

p38 What incident sparked the start of the First World War?

Inferential comprehension
p32 How does King Midas learn that gold is not the most important thing in life?

p33 Why does it matter that the man sees his daughter first when he gets home?

p38 Why is the description of the row of dominoes a good comparison to make?

Personal response
- Why do you think people like watching 'Mr Bean'?
- Do you think people should think about the consequences of their actions?
- Do you think the 'Chaos Theory' could be true?

Non-fiction features

p31 How does the text engage the reader from the start?

p35 Why is the information on this page set out as a flowchart?

p37 Why is a butterfly a suitable image for this page?

Published by Pearson Education Limited, Edinburgh Gate, Harlow, Essex, CM20 2JE.

www.pearsonschoolsandfecolleges.co.uk

Text © Pearson Education Limited 2012

Edited by Jo Dilloway
Designed by Tony Richardson and Siu Hang Wong
Original illustrations © Pearson Education Limited 2012
Illustrated by Sonia Possentini
Cover design by Siu Hang Wong
Cover illustration © Pearson Education Limited 2012

The right of Julia Golding to be identified as author of this work has been asserted by her in
accordance with the Copyright, Designs and Patents Act 1988.

First published 2012

16 15 14 13 12
10 9 8 7 6 5 4 3 2 1

British Library Cataloguing in Publication Data
A catalogue record for this book is available from the British Library

ISBN 978 0 435 07158 5

Printed at Scotprint, UK.

Acknowledgements
The author and publisher would like to thank the following individuals and organisations for
permission to reproduce photographs:

(Key: b-bottom; c-centre; l-left; r-right; t-top)

Corbis: Bettmann 32; Mary Evans Picture Library: Robert Hunt Library 38; Robert Harding World
Imagery: age fotostock / Mike Hill 37b; Shutterstock.com: Anson0618 37br, Monkey Business
Images 1, 31, Myn-Jhee 33; The Kobal Collection: Columbia / Marvel 34-35, Universal / Working
Title 36

Cover images: Back: Shutterstock.com: Anson0618

All other images © Pearson Education

Every effort has been made to contact copyright holders of material reproduced in this book. Any
omissions will be rectified in subsequent printings if notice is given to the publishers.